Contents

Answers to the questions are on the back of the Pull-out Poster in the centre of the book.

Published by Coordination Group Publications Ltd.

Contributors:
Angela Billington
Charley Darbishire
Chris Dennett
Katherine Stewart
Tim Wakeling
James Paul Wallis
Andrew Wright
Claire Thompson

ISBN 1 84146 261 6
Groovy website: www.cgpbooks.co.uk
Jolly bits of clipart from CorelDRAW
Printed by Elanders Hindson, Newcastle upon Tyne.

Organisms

An "organism" is a living thing. Plants and animals are organisms.

| These are animals... | ...and these are plants. |

Q1 All of these are organisms — write under each picture whether it is a plant or an animal.

Palm tree

Giraffe

Woman

Pine tree

....

Crab

Daisy

Ladybird

....

Q2 Organisms are plants or animals — are these organisms? Write "yes" or "no" under each.

Elephant

Car

Cactus

Chair

....

Lightning

Cockerel

Fly

Statue

....

Organism — is that an organization for organists...

There you go — it's the end of the first page. All you have to remember is that plants and animals are organisms. Besides that you have to be able to tell a plant from an animal — pretty easy stuff.

Where Animals Live

A habitat is the natural home for an organism — where it most likes to live.
For a <u>poppy</u>, it's a <u>grassy field</u>. <u>Worms</u> prefer <u>soil</u>.

Q1   Draw a line to join each of these animals to their habitat.
Some habitats are used more than once. I've done one for you.

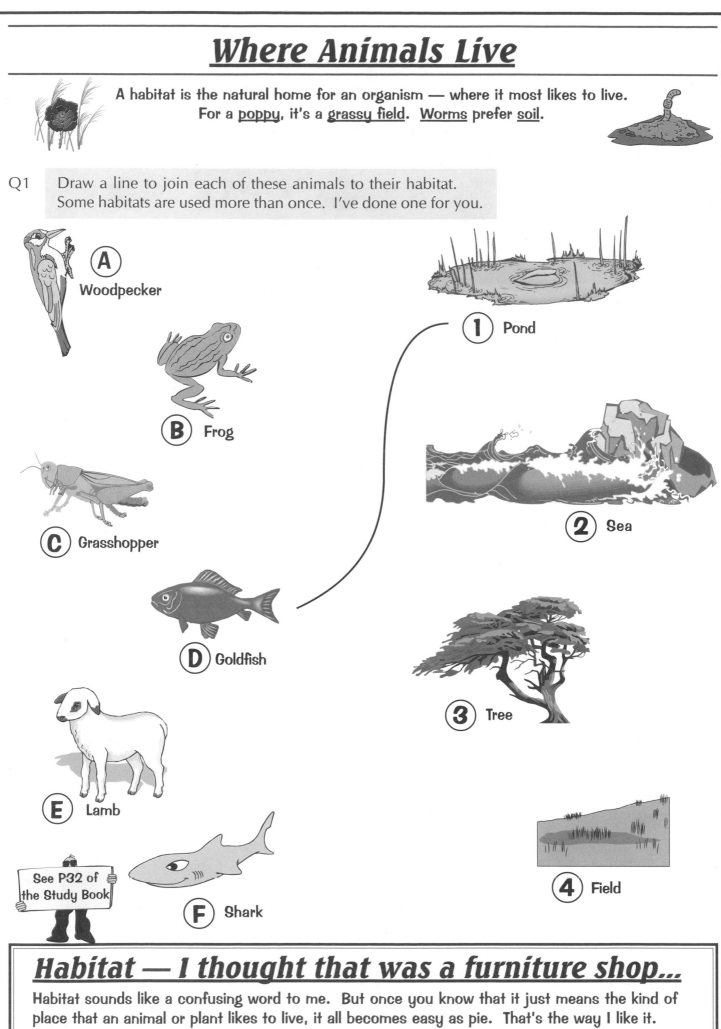

(A) Woodpecker

(B) Frog

(C) Grasshopper

(D) Goldfish

(E) Lamb

See P32 of the Study Book

(F) Shark

(1) Pond

(2) Sea

(3) Tree

(4) Field

Habitat — I thought that was a furniture shop...

Habitat sounds like a confusing word to me. But once you know that it just means the kind of place that an animal or plant likes to live, it all becomes easy as pie. That's the way I like it.

Different Kinds of Habitat

You find living things absolutely <u>everywhere</u> — ponds, fields, trees, hedges, flower beds, a patch of moss... or even under a stone.

Q1   Some habitats are big, some are small. Write "big" or "small" under these habitats.

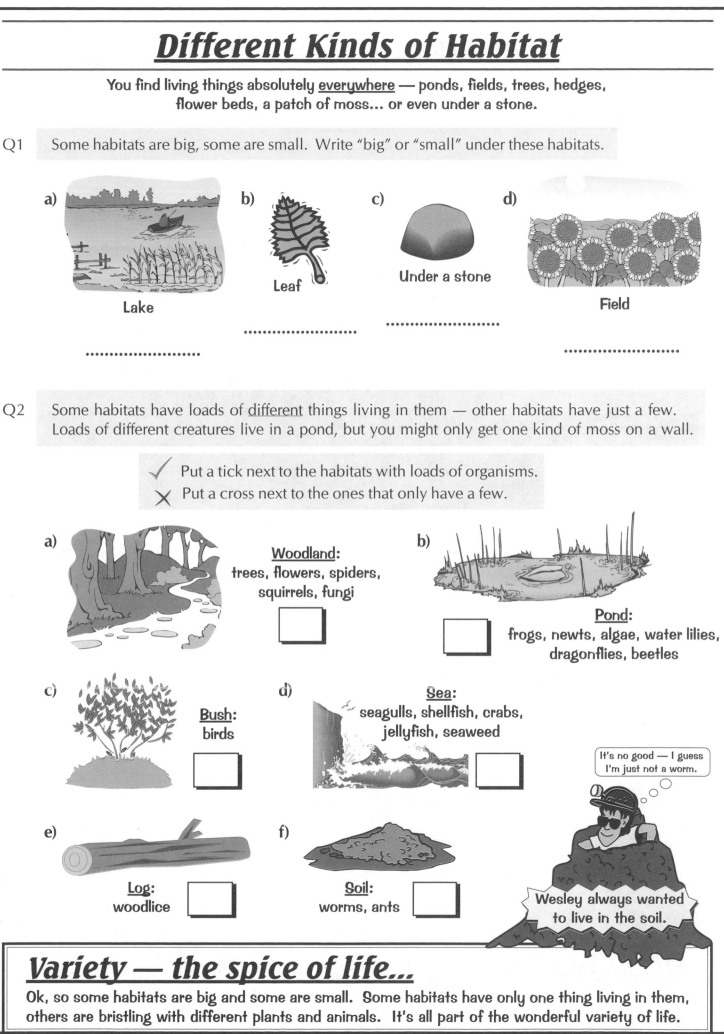

a)

Lake

....

b)

Leaf

....

c)

Under a stone

....

d)

Field

....

Q2   Some habitats have loads of <u>different</u> things living in them — other habitats have just a few.
Loads of different creatures live in a pond, but you might only get one kind of moss on a wall.

✓ Put a tick next to the habitats with loads of organisms.
✗ Put a cross next to the ones that only have a few.

a)

<u>Woodland:</u>
trees, flowers, spiders, squirrels, fungi

b)

<u>Pond:</u>
frogs, newts, algae, water lilies, dragonflies, beetles

c)

<u>Bush:</u>
birds

d)

<u>Sea:</u>
seagulls, shellfish, crabs, jellyfish, seaweed

It's no good — I guess I'm just not a worm.

e)

<u>Log:</u>
woodlice

f)

<u>Soil:</u>
worms, ants

Wesley always wanted to live in the soil.

Variety — the spice of life...

Ok, so some habitats are big and some are small. Some habitats have only one thing living in them, others are bristling with different plants and animals. It's all part of the wonderful variety of life.

Hunting Round the Garden

You can find wildlife just about anywhere you look. This morning I hunted around my garden — and found loads of interesting things living in it. There were frogs by my pond and woodlice under my crazy paving. Amazing — all that in <u>my garden</u>.

Q1 Here are all the creatures I found in my hunt. Count how many of each creature I found in each place and write the numbers in the table.

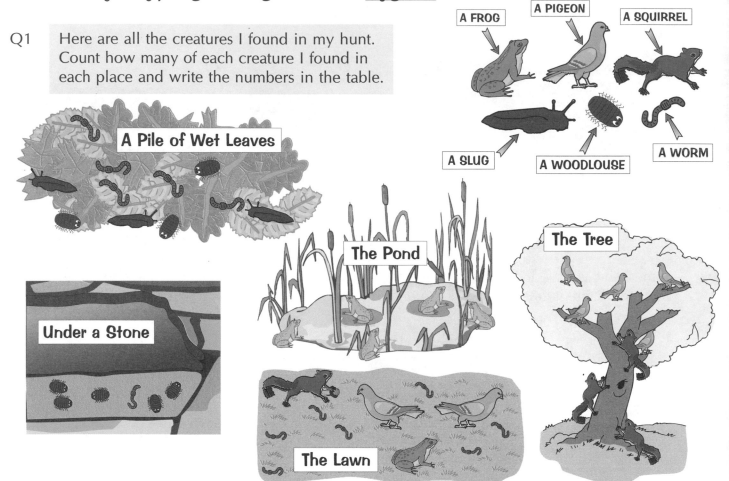

Remember — things that are smaller than you can get hurt more easily. You've got to be <u>really careful</u> with any creatures you find in your garden.

	In the Leaves	By the Pond	In the Tree	Under a Stone	On the Lawn
Woodlice					
Worms					
Slugs					
Squirrels					
Pigeons					
Frogs					

<u>All those crawly things — it sounds creepy to me...</u>

If you ever go finding little creatures like this, be mega-careful with them. They can be hurt really easily by clumping great human beings. And make sure you put them back where they came from.

Animals Live Where They Like To

Animals aren't stupid. They live in the places they <u>like</u> — that's where you'll find most of them. So you can <u>find out</u> where animals like to live by counting how many there are in different places.

Q1 This is a water beetle. It lives in or near to water, because it feeds on plants and animals which live in the water. Where would I find a water beetle in my garden?

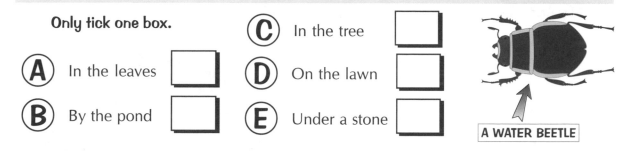

Only tick one box.

(A) In the leaves ☐

(B) By the pond ☐

(C) In the tree ☐

(D) On the lawn ☐

(E) Under a stone ☐

A WATER BEETLE

Q2 Animals mainly live where they prefer to. Look at the table on the last page and pick out where you think each creature prefers to live, and why you think they like to live there.

Write a letter and a number for each creature. You'll end up with two in the same habitat.

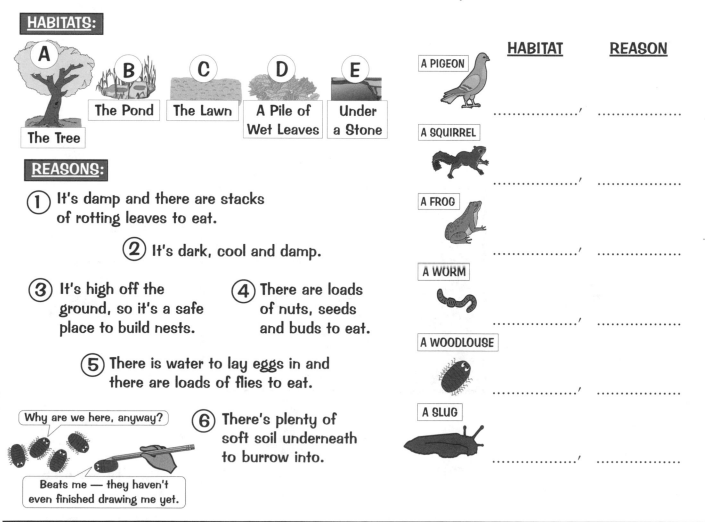

HABITATS:

(A) The Tree (B) The Pond (C) The Lawn (D) A Pile of Wet Leaves (E) Under a Stone

REASONS:

(1) It's damp and there are stacks of rotting leaves to eat.

(2) It's dark, cool and damp.

(3) It's high off the ground, so it's a safe place to build nests.

(4) There are loads of nuts, seeds and buds to eat.

(5) There is water to lay eggs in and there are loads of flies to eat.

(6) There's plenty of soft soil underneath to burrow into.

Why are we here, anyway?

Beats me — they haven't even finished drawing me yet.

HABITAT   REASON

A PIGEON .... , ...

A SQUIRREL .... , ...

A FROG .... , ...

A WORM .... , ...

A WOODLOUSE .... , ...

A SLUG .... , ...

Water Beetle — and what-a-beetle it is too...

Some like it hot, some like it cold, some like it waterlogged. Some animals need damp, cool conditions to survive, but some need it to be sunny, warm and dry. Funny old world, isn't it...

6

Pick the Best Animal for the Habitat

Some places are really great habitats for one animal — but ridiculous for another.
You'd never see an elephant swimming around deep in the ocean. On the other hand, you
wouldn't see a whale wandering around the Sahara Desert. It hasn't got feet, for a start...

Q1   In the soil it's damp and dark and there's loads of rotting stuff
to eat. One of these creatures lives in the soil — which is it?

....

A WORM

A COW

THE SOIL

A RAT

A SNAIL

Q2   In the desert, it's bone dry and really hot. Only two of
these animals can survive in the desert — which are they?

.... and

....

A PENGUIN

A CAMEL

THE DESERT

A RATTLESNAKE

A SHARK

A POODLE

I'd like to live in a pie — ah, you said DESERT...

Some animals live in odd places — like in the frozen Arctic or at the dry desert. That's where they
really want to be. Polar bears wouldn't like living in a nice warm place. They're mad, if you ask me.

Pick the Best Habitat for the Animal

All animals have features which help them survive in their natural habitat — like loads of fur or body fat for keeping warm, sharp teeth or claws for eating, or gills for surviving underwater.

Q1   Here are two different creatures. I've told you a bit about each one and you've got to work out where its natural habitat is.

a)   Where are you most likely to find this sheep?

A SHEEP

Eats grass and other plants.

Thick wool to keep warm.

Hooves are great for walking or running in hilly areas.

A CITY OR TOWN

A GRASSY HILL

A BEACH

b)   Where is this crab most likely to live?

A CRAB

My birthday's July 11th. That makes me a Cancer.

Legs developed for swimming and running.

Hard, waxy shell.

Eats small plants and animals that live in the sea.

THE WOODS

THE MOUNTAINS

THE SEASHORE

THESE BAGPIPES

Soggy leaves to you — a 5-star hotel to a slug...

Next time you see a creature somewhere near where you live, have a look at what helps it to survive there. You can generally tell just by looking at it. If you do see a sheep on the beach, it's lost.

8

Grouping Organisms

Everything that's alive is an organism — even plants. You can put organisms into groups by finding things they have in common. For example, you could put all animals that have four legs in a group, called "animals with four legs". Simple stuff, simple questions.

Q1   Draw a ring around each organism below that has a shell.

Snail   **Mussel**   **Man**   **Tortoise**

Blackbird   **Crab**   **Monkey**   **Ostrich**

Q2   All the organisms above that <u>aren't</u> circled have something in common. Fill in this sentence to say what it is.   They all have two ....

Q3   Here are six animals:

Octopus   **Butterfly**   **Mole**   **Bird**   **Spider**   **Worm**

In the boxes below, draw the animals which fit in each box.

They have wings:	They have 8 legs:	They live in the soil:

Read carefully — don't go gripping organists...

This sounds pretty scientific — "grouping organisms". But it's a doddle. All you have to do is pick out all the things with 4 legs, or with wings or whatever. That's all there is to it. No problem.

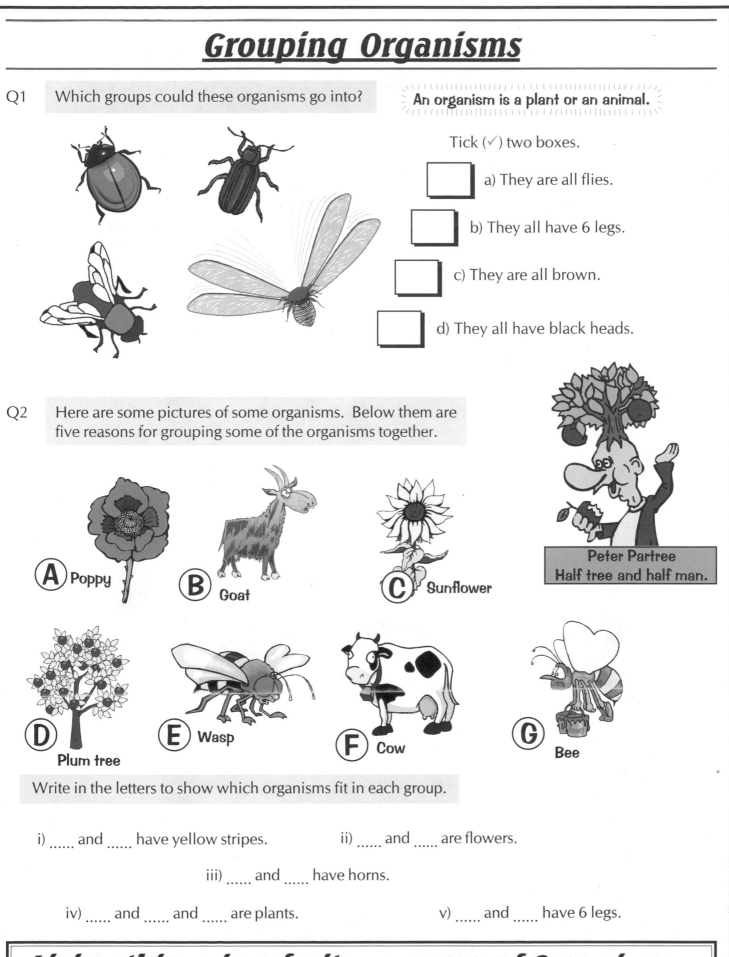

Grouping Organisms

Q1 Which groups could these organisms go into?

An organism is a plant or an animal.

Tick (✓) two boxes.

☐ a) They are all flies.

☐ b) They all have 6 legs.

☐ c) They are all brown.

☐ d) They all have black heads.

Q2 Here are some pictures of some organisms. Below them are five reasons for grouping some of the organisms together.

Ⓐ Poppy Ⓑ Goat Ⓒ Sunflower

Peter Partree
Half tree and half man.

Ⓓ Plum tree Ⓔ Wasp Ⓕ Cow Ⓖ Bee

Write in the letters to show which organisms fit in each group.

i) ..... and ..... have yellow stripes. ii) ..... and ..... are flowers.

iii) ..... and ..... have horns.

iv) ..... and ..... and ..... are plants. v) ..... and ..... have 6 legs.

Living things in a fruit — a grape of Organisms...

This is easy stuff — it's your chance to get an easy top mark. Once you've done these questions, go back and check each one. That's the only way to be sure you haven't made a daft mistake.

Using Keys to Identify Things

This is NOT to do with keys that unlock doors. You use these keys to find out the name of an organism by answering a few questions. Each question has two answers which lead you to a different question or to the name of the beastie. It's simpler than it sounds, so get cracking.

Q1   Here's an example of a key you can use to find the names of three organisms below.

1) Does it have orange stripes? YES — it's a Centipede.
                                 NO — go to question 2).

   2) Does it have two crab-like claws? YES — it's a Scorpion.
                                          NO — it's a Silverfish.

Take one creature at a time. Start at 1) and go through the questions until the answer gives you a name.

I've already done 'A' — you find out the names of 'B' and 'C'.

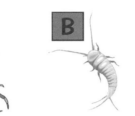
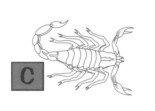

A *Centipede* ....

B ....

C ....

Q2   This time there are five organisms to find the names of. Just like Q1, take one at a time and go through the questions until you find its name — then fill it in.

See page 30 of the Study Book

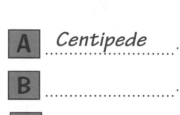

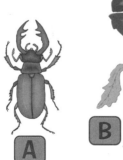

1) Is it a plant? YES   go to question 2).
                  NO   go to question 3).

2) Does it have a red flower? YES — it's a Poppy.
                                NO   it's a Sunflower.

3) Does it have a tail? YES — it's a Newt.
                          NO go to question 4).

4) Has it got a brown back?   YES — it's a Stag Beetle.
                                NO — it's a Great Diving Beetle.

A ....

B ....

C ....

D ....

E ....

Keys to identify things? — I use them to open locks...

The golden rule when you use a key is to take one organism at a time. Answer the questions until you get to its name — then check it by going through the questions again. Bish, bash, bosh, it's done.

Using Keys to Identify Things

The thing below with boxes and arrows is called a branched key. It's only a tiny bit different from the keys on page 10. You take one organism at a time and answer the first question — if the answer is "yes", follow the branch that says "YES". If the answer is "no", follow the branch that says "NO". Each branch will take you to another question or to the name of the organism.

Q1   Find the name of all these organisms using the branched key.

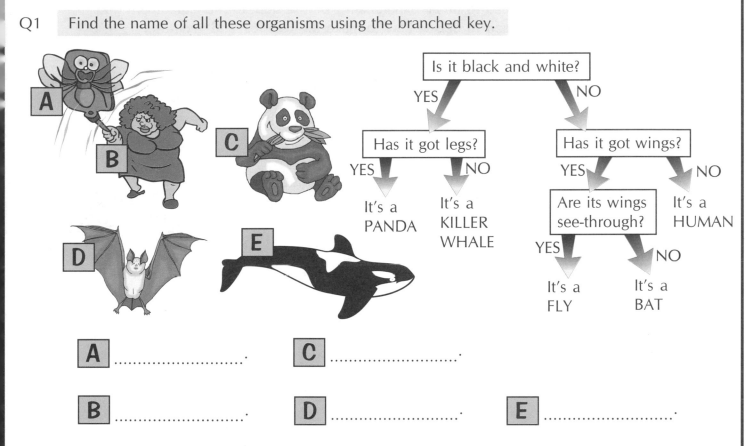

Is it black and white?

YES   NO

Has it got legs?

YES   NO

It's a PANDA

It's a KILLER WHALE

Has it got wings?

YES   NO

Are its wings see-through?

It's a HUMAN

YES   NO

It's a FLY

It's a BAT

A ....
C ....

B ....
D ....
E ....

Q2   Now you've used a few keys — have a go at adding the questions to this one.

Fill in the blanks using the questions in the yellow boxes.

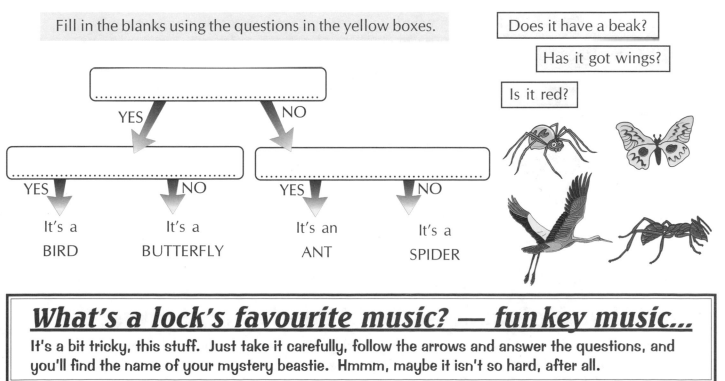

Does it have a beak?

Has it got wings?

Is it red?

YES   NO

YES   NO   YES   NO

It's a BIRD

It's a BUTTERFLY

It's an ANT

It's a SPIDER

What's a lock's favourite music? — fun key music...

It's a bit tricky, this stuff. Just take it carefully, follow the arrows and answer the questions, and you'll find the name of your mystery beastie. Hmmm, maybe it isn't so hard, after all.

Mini Project 1 — What Woodlice Like

PROJECT ONE — Find out if woodlice prefer damp or dry conditions.

To test whether or not woodlice prefer damp or dry conditions you need to do an experiment. Before you do the experiment you need to decide how to make the test fair and accurate.

Q1 Read each sentence below. For each one, tick the box to say if you think it is "important" or "not important". If it could change the result of the experiment, then it's important.

a) All the woodlice are the same size.

IMPORTANT [ ] NOT IMPORTANT [ ]

b) There is a damp place and a dry place.

IMPORTANT [ ] NOT IMPORTANT [ ]

c) More than one woodlouse is used.

IMPORTANT [ ] NOT IMPORTANT [ ]

HINT:
Listen to me. Size doesn't matter.

d) The woodlice should all be given names, like Mildred or Agatha.

IMPORTANT [ ] NOT IMPORTANT [ ]

e) The woodlice are all the same shade of grey.

IMPORTANT [ ] NOT IMPORTANT [ ]

f) The tank where the woodlice are kept is made of glass.

IMPORTANT [ ] NOT IMPORTANT [ ]

Q2 The length of time you leave the woodlice before getting the result <u>is important</u>.

Tick one of the options below and then give one reason why you picked it.

Only choose one.

Come on guys 5 seconds to go!

Phew, I'm zonked, me.

[ ] We should leave them for 10 seconds.

[ ] We should leave them for at least a year.

[ ] We should count how many are on each side after 20 minutes, 40 minutes and 60 minutes.

Reason: ....

....

Woodlouse cinema — you'd need a mini projector...

Woodlice — look under stones and rotting logs and you'll soon find enough of these armour-plated beasties for the experiment. Just remember to put them back where you found them at the end.

KS2 Science Answers — Habitats

Q4: 37, 2, 1

Page 14 Habitat Testing — Mini Project 2

Q1

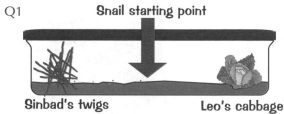

Snail starting point

Sinbad's twigs   Leo's cabbage

Q2: a) Not important

b) Important

c) Not important

d) Important

Page 15 Habitat Testing — Mini Project 2

Q1

Time	Number of snails		
	On the twigs	Middle	On the cabbage
0 hours	0	30	0
5 hours	5	17	8
10 hours	2	13	15
20 hours	2	7	21

Q2: 21, 2, cabbage

Q3: Look to see if the cabbage has any bits missing from it (ie parts of it have been eaten).

Page 16 Plants and Animals — Organism

Q1: Rabbit.

Q2: Grass and Lettuce

Q3: Vole and Sparrow.

Page 17 Plants and Animals — Organism

Q1: There are no fish in the woods.

Q2: It's too cold for them.

Q3: Lizards live ... in hot dry places.

Crocodiles live ... near warm water.

Penguins live ... in cold icy places.

Horses live ... where there's grass.

Page 18 Predators and Prey

Q1: a) Blackbird

b) Fox

c) Heron

d) Spider

Q2: Lion to Zebra, Cat to Mouse, Wolf to Lamb, Frog to Slug.

Page 19 Food Chains

Q1: Arrows from Slug to Frog, and Frog to Heron.

Arrows from Soil to Worm, Worm to Blackbird, and Blackbird to Hawk.

Q2: Leaf to Beetle to Mouse to Owl.

Page 20 Food Chains

Q1: a) Dandelion to Rabbit to Fox

b) Plant to Bugs to Minnows to Otter

Page 21 Food Chains

Q1: Any green plant

Q2: The beginnings of these food chains are all "green plants".

Page 22 The Environment Needs Protection

Q1: Tommy stole the *plants* from the pond. The tadpoles *died*.

The fish couldn't survive when he took away the *water*.

When he took away the *fish* the *heron* couldn't hunt.

Q2: Penguin - cold, light, wet.

Worm - dark, cold, wet.

Snail - cold, dark, wet.

Snake - dry, warm, light.

Q3: a) He'd leave in search of a darker place.

b) He'd leave in search of a leafier place. No food.

Page 23 The Environment Needs Protection

Q1: Dear Mr. Sockmaster,

Please don't drain the pixie lake. The fish will die and so the heron will have nothing to eat. The ducks will go away because they will have no duckweed to eat. Please leave the animals' lake alone.

Yours sincerely,

A. Random Pupil.

(Accept any sensible answer.)

Page 24 Revision Questions

Q1:   Has it got a flower?

Has it got yellow petals?   Does it have eyes?

Q2: B and C

Q3: The sea

Q4: Pond weed ➡ Pond snails ➡ Minnows ➡ Perch

Q5: Spider   Shark

Page 25 Revision Questions

Q6: They all live in the sea: shrimp, fish, whale

Second box: cow, mouse, giraffe

Any sensible answer for the title is ok, eg "They all live on land" or "They all have four legs".

Q7: Mouse

Q8: Giraffe

Q9: There isn't any fish to eat.

Q10: A pond

Q11: Because the heron eats fish.

Q12: Any sensible answer e.g. "pond snails".

FOOD CHAINS

Hawk

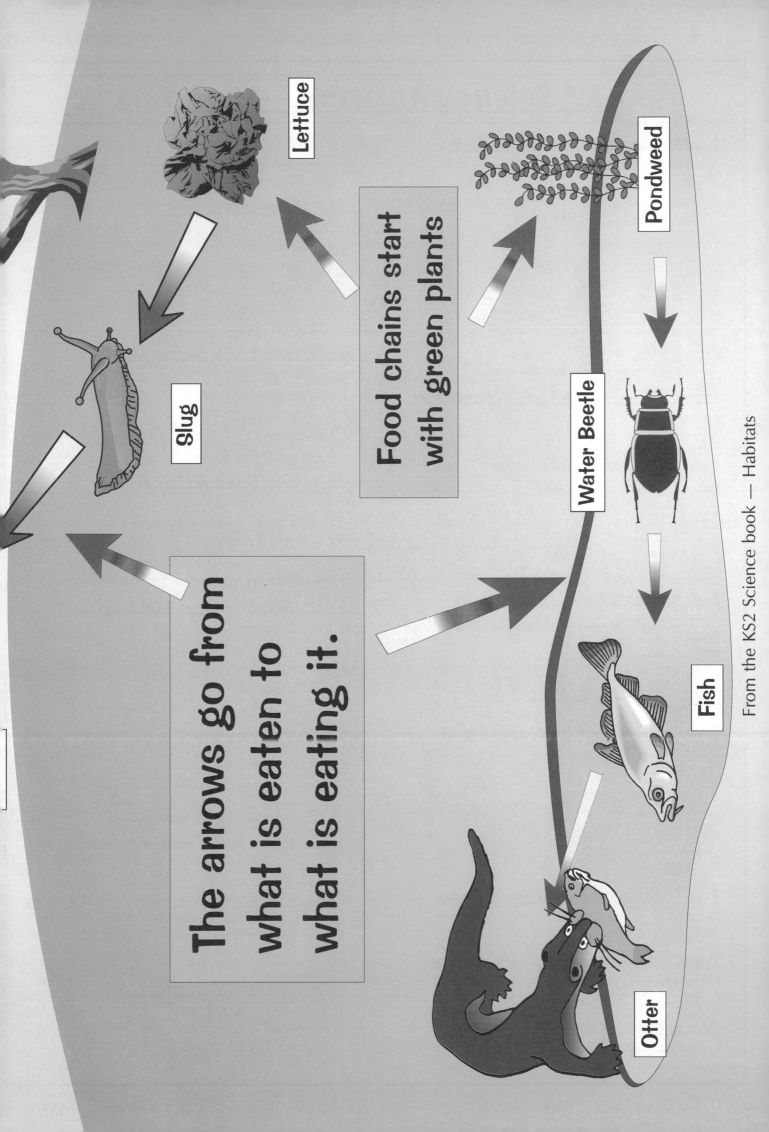

Lettuce

Slug

Food chains start
with green plants

The arrows go from
what is eaten to
what is eating it.

Pondweed

Water Beetle

Fish

Otter

KS2 Science Answers — Habitats

Page 1 Plants & Animals — Organisms

Q1: Palm tree — plant
Giraffe — animal
Woman — animal
Pine tree — plant
Crab — animal
Daisy — plant
Ladybird — animal

Q2: Elephant — yes   Lightning — no
Car — no   Cockerel — yes
Cactus — yes   Fly — yes
Chair — no   Statue — no

Page 2 Where Animals Live — Their Habitat

Q1: A — 3   B — 1   C — 4
D — 1   E — 4   F — 2

Page 3 Different Kinds of Habitat

Q1: a) big   b) small
c) small   d) big

Q2: a) tick   b) tick
c) cross   d) tick
e) cross   f) cross

Page 4 Hunting Round the Garden

	In the Leaves	By the Pond	In the Tree	Under a Stone	On the Lawn
Woodlice	3			5	
Worms	5		1		7
Slugs	3				
Squirrels			3		1
Pigeons			5		2
Frogs		5			1

Page 5 Animals Live Where They Like to

Q1: B
Q2: Pigeon — A, 3
Squirrel — A, 4
Frog — B, 5
Worm — C, 6
Woodlouse — E, 2
Slug — D, 1

Page 6 Pick the best animal for the habitat

Q1: Worm
Q2: Camel, Rattlesnake

Page 7 Pick the best animal for the habitat

Q1: a) A grassy hill
b) The seashore

Page 8 Grouping Organisms

Q1: Snail, clam, tortoise, hermit crab.
Q2: They all have two legs (or eyes etc).

Page 9 Grouping Organisms

Q3: They have wings: Butterfly, bird.
They have 8 legs: Octopus, spider.
They live in the soil: Mole, worm.

Q1: (b) and (c).
Q2: i) E and G.
ii) A and C.
iii) B and F.
iv) A and C and D.
v) E and G.

Page 10 Using Keys to Identify Things

Q1: B — Silverfish
C — Scorpion
Q2: A — Stag Beetle   B — Poppy
C — Newt   D — Sunflower
E — Great Diving Beetle

Page 11 Using Keys to Identify Things

Q1: A — Fly   D — Bat
B — Human   E — Killer Whale
C — Panda
Q2:   Has it got wings?
Does it have a beak?   Is it Red?

Page 12 Habitat Testing — Mini Project 1

Q1: a) Not important
b) Important
c) Important
d) Not important
e) Not important
f) Not important

Q2: Count how many are on each side
after 20, 40 and 60 minutes.
Reason: 10 seconds wouldn't be long enough,
and a year would be far too long.
(Accept any sensible answer.)

Page 13 Habitat Testing — Mini Project 1

Q1: 2
Q2: between 5 and 25.
Reason: It would be difficult to count them, it would
be difficult to keep them under control, the
experiment would take too long.
(Accept any sensible answer.)

Q3:

Time	Number of Woodlice		
	Damp Side	Middle	Dry Side
0 minutes	0	40	0
20 minutes	20	12	8
40 minutes	32	5	3
60 minutes	37	2	1

Mini Project 1 — What Woodlice Like

Q1 Where would you put all the woodlice?

Circle ①, ② or ③.

DAMP   DRY

①   ②   ③

Q2 How many woodlice should you use in the experiment? Tick one of the options below.

1 ☐   between 5 and 25 ☐   4,637 ☐   more than 1,000,000 ☐

Why do you think it would be a bad idea to use too many woodlice?

Reason: ....

....

Q3 Frankie has already done this experiment. She wrote down how many woodlice were in each bit of the tank, after 0 minutes, 20 minutes, 40 minutes and 60 minutes.

Time	Number of Woodlice		
	Damp Side	Middle	Dry Side
0 minutes	0	40	0
20 minutes	....	....	....
40 minutes	32	5	3
60 minutes	37	2	1

Tommy wasn't like the other woodlice.

Where's Tommy?

After twenty minutes there were twenty woodlice in the damp bit of the tank, twelve in the middle bit and eight in the dry bit.

Finish Frankie's table by putting in the second row of numbers.

Q4 The sentence below sums up the results of the experiment.

Fill in the gaps in the sentence using numbers from the table above.

"After 60 minutes there were .... woodlice in the damp area, ... woodlice in the middle and .... woodlice in the dry area. So woodlice prefer .... **conditions**."

Scientific breath freshener — experimint...

Phew. After that lot you deserve a rest.

Mini Project 2 — What Snails Like

PROJECT TWO — Finding out if snails prefer Sinbad's twigs or Leo's cabbages.

Sinbad and Leo both like feeding snails. Sinbad reckons that snails prefer his twigs because they're really tasty. Leo says that snails can't resist his cabbages because they're far tastier. They decide to do an experiment to prove once and for all whether snails find twigs or cabbages the tastiest.

Q1 This time you're going to design the tank where the experiment is going to take place. Follow all the instructions from a) to e).

This is the empty tank.

a) Draw in where you would put Sinbad's twigs and where you would put Leo's cabbage.

b) Label the drawings "Sinbad's twigs" and "Leo's cabbage".

c) Draw an arrow to where you would put the snails to start with.

d) Label the arrow "snail starting point".

e) Draw a lid on the tank to stop the little blighters escaping.

Show me the FOOD!

Q2 Decide which of these sentences are important to the experiment. Read each one, decide if it's important or not and then tick the right box.

	IMPORTANT	NOT IMPORTANT
The twigs and the lettuce are labelled so we know the difference.	☐	☐
The snails are given more time than the woodlice.	☐	☐
All the snails have different types of shell.	☐	☐
The same amount of twigs and cabbage is used.	☐	☐

What do sporty snails wear? — shell suits...

Snails come in all shapes and sizes — some live on the land, some in the sea and others live in lakes and rivers. Only use land snails for this experiment — you'll find 'em where it's dark and wet.

Mini Project 2 — What Snails Like

Zeta wrote down the results of the experiment in her note pad. She wrote down the number of snails in each part of the tank at four different times.

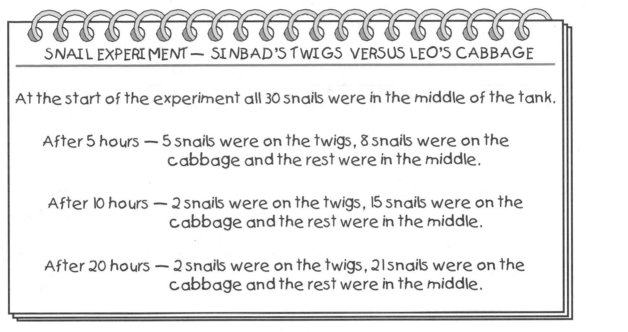

SNAIL EXPERIMENT — SINBAD'S TWIGS VERSUS LEO'S CABBAGE

At the start of the experiment all 30 snails were in the middle of the tank.

After 5 hours — 5 snails were on the twigs, 8 snails were on the cabbage and the rest were in the middle.

After 10 hours — 2 snails were on the twigs, 15 snails were on the cabbage and the rest were in the middle.

After 20 hours — 2 snails were on the twigs, 21 snails were on the cabbage and the rest were in the middle.

Q1 Put the results from Zeta's notepad into the table below.

Time	Number of snails		
	On the twigs	Middle	On the cabbage

Ladybirds tell the worst jokes

Q2 Fill in the gaps in the sentence below to show the result of the experiment.

"After 20 hours there were .... snails on Leo's cabbage and only .... snails on Sinbad's twigs. So the snails prefer Leo's ...."

Q3 Sinbad isn't at all happy. He still thinks that the snails prefer his twigs to eat. He says that they only like to go to sleep on Leo's cabbage.

Suggest a way they could check if the snails had been eating the cabbage.

....

How do hi-tech snails keep in touch — e-snail...

People kill snails with horrible pellets because they munch a lot of plants. You don't have to kill them! You can circle plants with gravel or use smelly plants to keep the snails away. Save the snail. ☺

16

What Animals Eat

Animals have to eat to live — and most animals can only eat certain types of things.

Cows eat grass... they <u>don't</u> eat fish.

Blackbirds eat worms... they <u>don't</u> eat rabbits.

Q1   Write down which of these things a fox would eat.

Mmm... tasty

Rabbit

Turnip

Cow

....

Q2   Tick which two of these things a rabbit would eat.

Chicken ☐   Grass ☐   Lettuce ☐

Cor... I fancy a bit of that.

Q3   Write down which two of these things a cat would eat.

Delicious.

Wood

Vole

Sparrow

....

Food, glorious food...

Most humans will eat loads of different types of food, but animals generally stick to only one or two things. It'd be like you only ever eating roast beef. Sounds seriously boring to me, but there you go.

What Animals Eat

Animals can only live in certain places, because they can only eat certain things.
It's no good them trying to live in a place where they can't get food — they'd starve.

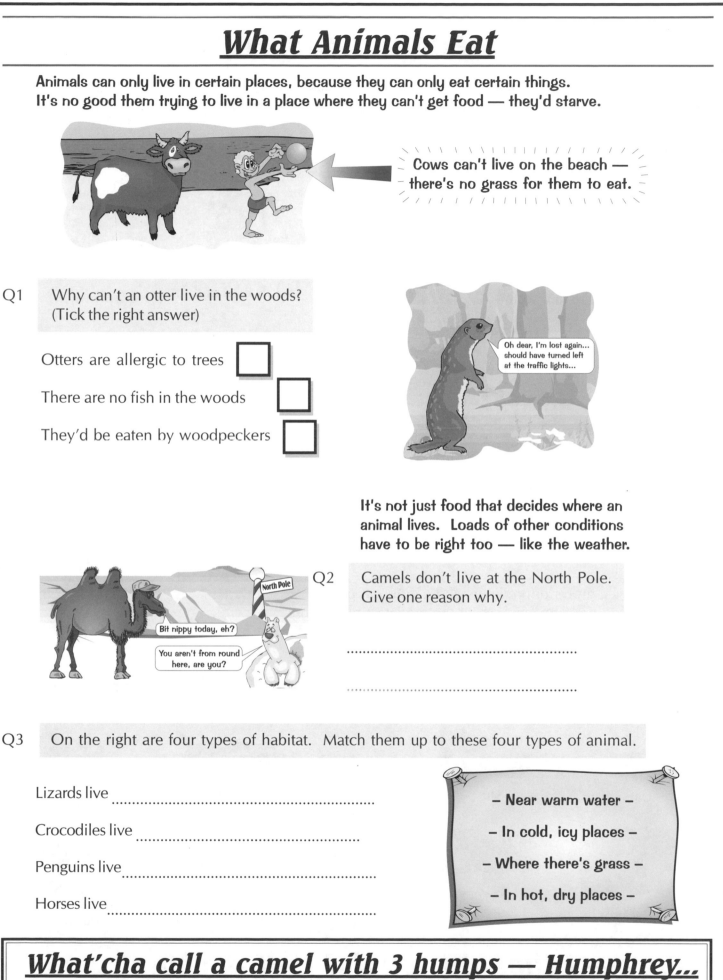

Cows can't live on the beach —
there's no grass for them to eat.

Q1 Why can't an otter live in the woods?
(Tick the right answer)

Otters are allergic to trees ☐

There are no fish in the woods ☐

They'd be eaten by woodpeckers ☐

Oh dear, I'm lost again...
should have turned left
at the traffic lights...

It's not just food that decides where an
animal lives. Loads of other conditions
have to be right too — like the weather.

Q2 Camels don't live at the North Pole.
Give one reason why.

North Pole

Bit nippy today, eh?

You aren't from round
here, are you?

....

....

Q3 On the right are four types of habitat. Match them up to these four types of animal.

Lizards live ....

Crocodiles live ....

Penguins live ....

Horses live ....

– Near warm water –

– In cold, icy places –

– Where there's grass –

– In hot, dry places –

What'cha call a camel with 3 humps — Humphrey...

If you want to know what type of place an animal likes, just think of where it does live. That'll be
what it likes. Most of the rest's just common sense. And you've got bags of that, haven't you...

Predators and Prey

Some organisms are predators, some are prey — some are both.
The predator <u>eats</u> the prey, and the prey <u>gets eaten</u> by the predator.

Q1　Here are some pairs of predators and their prey.
For each pair, write down which one is the predator.

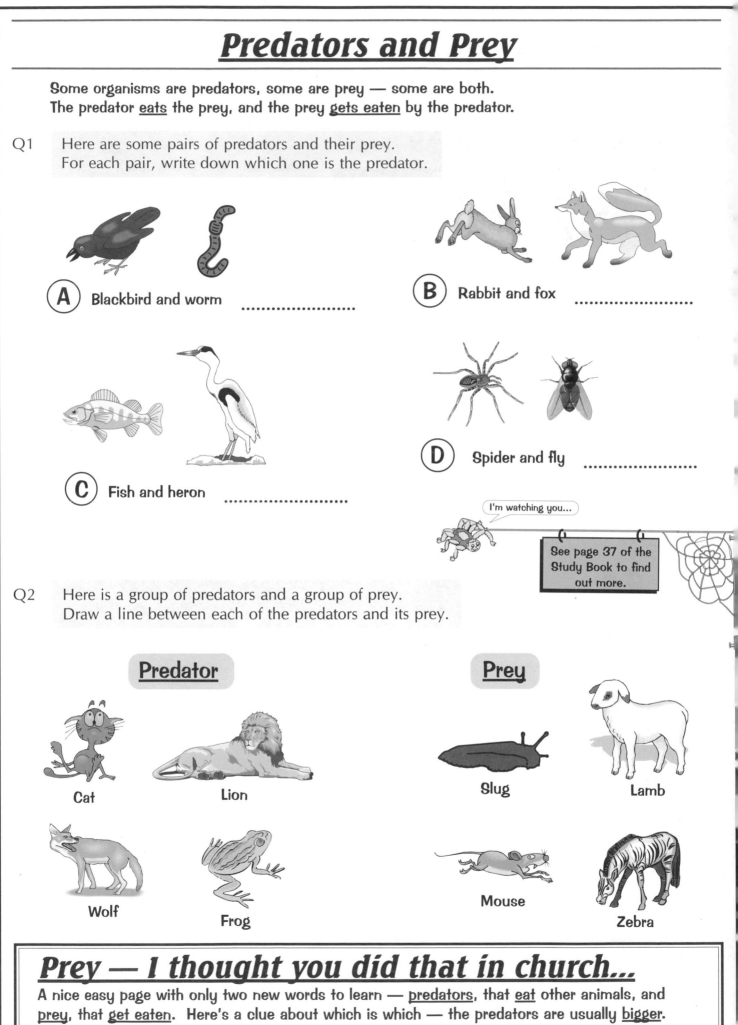

(A) Blackbird and worm ....

(B) Rabbit and fox ....

(C) Fish and heron ....

(D) Spider and fly ....

I'm watching you...

See page 37 of the
Study Book to find
out more.

Q2　Here is a group of predators and a group of prey.
Draw a line between each of the predators and its prey.

Predator

Cat　　Lion

Wolf　　Frog

Prey

Slug　　Lamb

Mouse　　Zebra

<u>Prey — I thought you did that in church...</u>

A nice easy page with only two new words to learn — <u>predators</u>, that <u>eat</u> other animals, and
<u>prey</u>, that <u>get eaten</u>. Here's a clue about which is which — the predators are usually <u>bigger</u>.

Food Chains

A <u>food chain</u> shows which animals eat which other animals (or plants).

Plants <u>don't</u> eat things. A food chain <u>starts</u> with <u>what gets eaten</u> and the arrows point towards <u>what does the eating</u>. Got it?

Remember, the food chain only goes in <u>one</u> direction.

Did you say "food chain"?

Q1 Fill in the arrows for these food chains. Follow the example.

Derek's muddled again...

① Lettuce ② Slug ③ Frog ④ Heron

① Soil ② Worm ③ Blackbird ④ Hawk

See page 36 of the Study Book to find out more.

Q2 Here is a food chain with the organisms in the wrong order.
Write their names in the right order in the spaces between the arrows.

.... ➤ .... ➤ .... ➤ ....

Owl   Leaf   Mouse   Beetle

Food chains — not about burger restaurants...

When you're looking at a food chain, remember that they always <u>start</u> with a <u>plant</u> that gives food to an <u>animal</u>. The animal gets eaten by a bigger one, the bigger one gets eaten... you get the idea.

Food Chains

The plants are called <u>producers</u>, because they make their own food inside themselves.

The animals are called <u>consumers</u>, because they consume (eat) food.

Q1 Make a food chain for each of these sets of organisms. Draw one organism in each box.

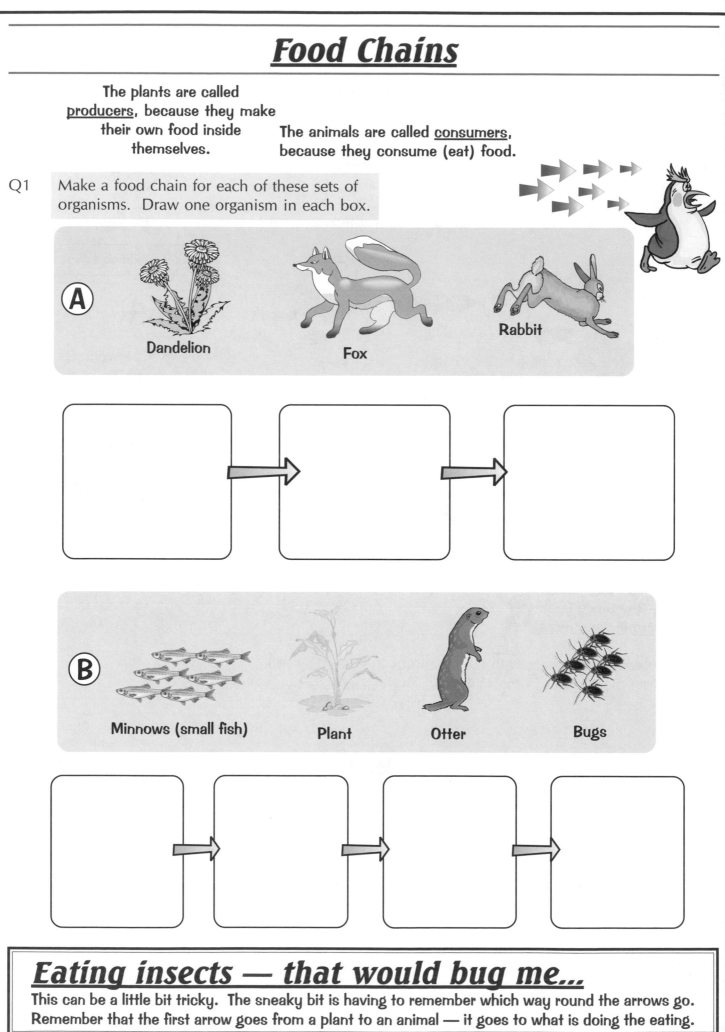

A
Dandelion   Fox   Rabbit

B
Minnows (small fish)   Plant   Otter   Bugs

<u>Eating insects — that would bug me...</u>

This can be a little bit tricky. The sneaky bit is having to remember which way round the arrows go. Remember that the first arrow goes from a plant to an animal — it goes to what is doing the eating.

Food Chains

Q1   Most food chains start with a green plant. Fill in the first organism in this food chain (the caterpillar might give you a clue).

.... → **Caterpillar** → **Robin** → **Eagle**

Q2   Here are some more food chains. What do the beginnings of these food chains have in common?

Think about whether it is a plant or an animal, and what colour it is...

① **River plant** → ② **Bugs** → ③ **Trout** → ④ **Heron**

① **Grass** → ② **Mouse** → ③ **Owl**

① **Trees** → ② **Green flies** → ③ **Ladybird** → ④ **Blackbird** → *Mmmm — More food!*

Answer: The beginnings of these food chains are all ....

Get this knowledge planted in your head...
I reckon that's enough of food chains. On to something new on the next page. I can hardly wait...

The Environment Needs Protection

Each animal lives in a place that suits it best. It's a good idea not to change its habitat too much — you could scare them away. You might even kill it.

Q1   Fill in the gaps in the tale of Tommy the Tinkerer. Use the words below.

Tommy stole the .... from the pond. The tadpoles ....

The fish couldn't survive when he took away the ....

When he took away the .... the .... couldn't hunt.

water	heron	died	fish	plants

Q2   Draw lines from each animal to its favourite conditions listed below. Follow the example.

dry   cold   warm   dark   wet   light

Q3   The council wants to clean Dave Woodlouse's home.
What would Dave do if...

a) A light was added? ....
....

b) The old leaves were tidied away?

....

....

....

The council cleans Dave Woodlouse's home

My ideal habitat — luxury flat, indoor swimming pool...

Different animals like different habitats. Woodlice like it to be damp and cool. Snakes like things to be hot and dry. Each animal likes things to be its own way. So leave it like that.

The Environment Needs Protection

Lionel Sockmaster is a pixie with crazy plans. Last year he wanted to cut down the forest. The Pixie Council had to send him this letter to stop him:

Lionel wanted to cut down the forest

Dear Mr. Sockmaster,

Please don't cut down the trees. The birds will have nowhere to nest. The caterpillars will have no leaves to eat. The squirrels will have no acorns to gather. Please leave the animals' habitat alone.

Yours sincerely,

The Pixie Council.

Q1 Now Lionel wants to drain the pixie lake. Write a letter telling him why he shouldn't, using the space below. There are some ideas on the right.

Dear Mr. Sockmaster,
....
....
....
....
....
....
....
....
....
Yours sincerely,
....
....

water-lilies

fish   frogs   ducks

duckweed

heron

Lionel tries to drain the lake

Pick your favourite letter — I'd pixie... *pick C — geddit...*

Animals have their favourite kind of places to live. If you messed around with them, it'd be like someone coming and changing your house around while you were out. Don't mess with them.

Revision Questions

These two pages cover bits from all over the book. The questions will help you to check that you really know your stuff. Get your pen ready, get your brain in gear and storm through this lot.

Q1   Have a go at filling in the questions on this branched key.

Fill in the blanks using the questions in the yellow boxes.

Has it got yellow petals?

Does it have eyes?

Has it got a flower?

....
      YES   NO

....
  YES   NO   YES   NO

It's a   It's a   It's a   It's a
BUTTERCUP   ROSE   CROCODILE   JELLYFISH

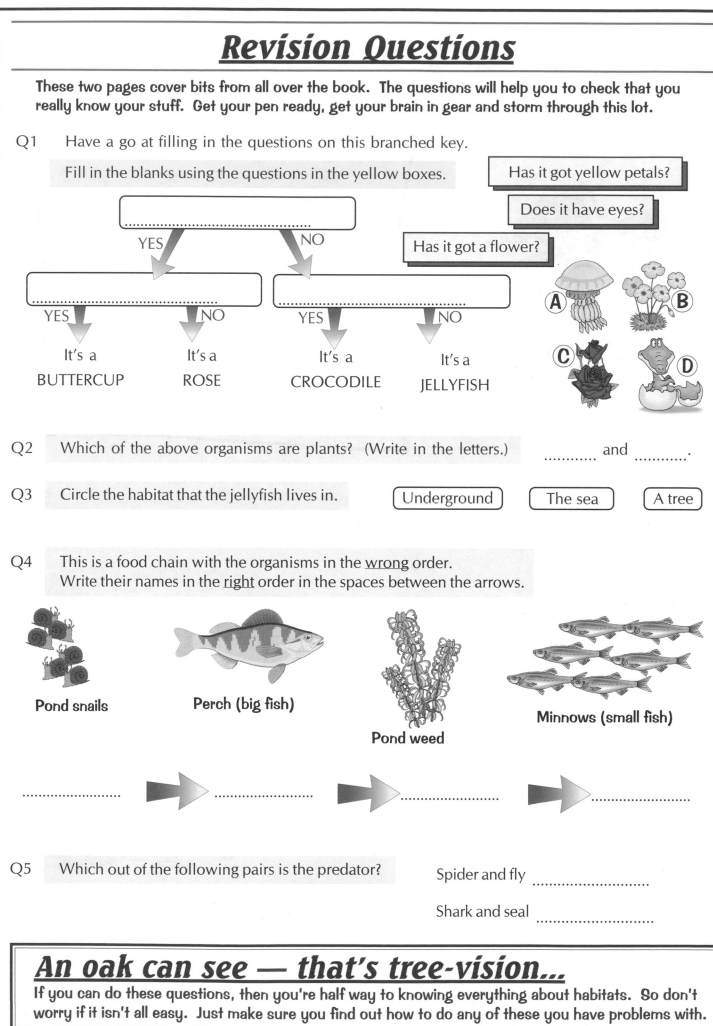

Q2   Which of the above organisms are plants? (Write in the letters.)   .... and ....

Q3   Circle the habitat that the jellyfish lives in.   Underground   The sea   A tree

Q4   This is a food chain with the organisms in the <u>wrong</u> order.
     Write their names in the <u>right</u> order in the spaces between the arrows.

Pond snails   **Perch (big fish)**   **Pond weed**   **Minnows (small fish)**

.... → .... → .... → ....

Q5   Which out of the following pairs is the predator?

Spider and fly ....

Shark and seal ....

An oak can see — that's tree-vision...

If you can do these questions, then you're half way to knowing everything about habitats. So don't worry if it isn't all easy. Just make sure you find out how to do any of these you have problems with.

Revision Questions

Q6

Shrimp   Fish   Cow   Whale   Mouse   Giraffe

They all live in the sea:	.... :

Put the names of the animals that live in the sea in the first box.
Put the names of the rest of the organisms in the second box.
Think of something all the animals in the second box have in common. Put it as a title here.

Q7   Which of the organisms at the top of the page would a fox eat?   ....

Q8   Which of the organisms at the top of a page would eat leaves from trees?   ....

Q9   Why don't polar bears live in a forest? (Tick the right answer.)

It's too cold for them. ☐   There aren't any fish to eat. ☐   They hate birdsong. ☐

Q10   Which of the following places is the frog's habitat? (Tick the right answer.)

?

The sea ☐   A pond ☐   The desert ☐

Q11   If the pond is drained the fish will die. Why will the heron go hungry if the pond is drained?   ....

Q12   Name one other organism that would be affected if the pond was drained. (It doesn't have to be an animal.)   ....

Where's the habitat? — around the Monk...

That's it. The end of the book. If you can do all the stuff on this page and the one before it, then you've learnt everything about habitats. If there are bits you can't do, it's a good idea to look them up.

Index